Nan...
and Games

a play by Julia Donaldson

for Jesse

illustrated by
Robert Bartelt

The four children in this play – Jamie, Robin, Helen and Tanim – are all in the same class at school. Each scene of the play takes place in their school playground during a different playtime on the same day.

Robin is a very bossy boy. This may be because at home his two big brothers boss him about. He has plenty of good ideas for exciting games, but the trouble is that he always wants to take the best parts himself. A lot of children don't want to play with Robin for this reason. Usually he just plays with his best friend Jamie. Robin is not very good at school games or running, and sometimes he gets teased because of this.

Jamie, Robin's best friend, is quite a shy boy but he is not afraid of saying what he thinks. He doesn't much like joining in big games of football. He prefers the same sort of adventure games that Robin likes. He finds Robin fun and likes the way he is so full of ideas. At first Jamie did whatever Robin told him, but now he is beginning to get fed up with Robin's bossy ways.

Helen and Tanim have been friends ever since they were in reception class.

Helen, who has no brothers or sisters, is very keen for Tanim to be her best friend. In fact, she is rather jealous if Tanim plays with anyone else and she doesn't like letting other people into their games. She is not bossy like Robin is, but she sometimes tries to hurt people by calling them names.

Tanim comes from a big family and has no trouble making friends. She likes playing with Helen, but she would rather play with a bigger group of people. Unlike Helen, she would like to join in Robin's and Jamie's games. Tanim is not very good at sticking up for herself or other people.

Names and Games

SCENE 1

The school playground, at morning play.

(Enter Robin and Jamie.)

Robin: Hi, Jamie.

Jamie: Hi, Robin. What shall we play today?

Robin: Robin Hood, of course.

Jamie: All right. I'll be Robin Hood then.

Robin: *(Bossily)* No you can't. I'm Robin Hood. I'm always Robin Hood, remember?

Jamie: That's not fair. Why should you always be Robin Hood?

Robin: Because my name really *is* Robin.

Jamie: Well, who shall I be then?

Robin: Little John, of course.

Jamie: But I'm sick of being Little John all the time. He just gets bossed about by Robin Hood.

Robin: All right, be Friar Tuck then.

Jamie: Who's he?

Robin: He's this big fat guy who eats all the time.

Jamie: That sounds more like you.

Robin: I'm not fat.

Jamie: I didn't say you were fat, I just said ...

Robin: *(Noticing Helen and Tanim coming towards them)*
Be quiet, Little John – someone's coming!
Let's hide, then we can spring out on them
and take all their gold.
(Robin and Jamie hide. Enter Helen and Tanim.)

Tanim: Hi, Helen.

Helen: Hi, Tanim. What shall we play today?

Tanim: How about Tunnel Tig?

Helen: I've forgotten how you play that.

Tanim: You know, it's that game where you crawl under people's legs to set them free when they've been caught.

Helen: Oh yes, that's good. Who's going to be It?

Tanim: Let's dip.
(She "dips", starting with Helen.)

Tanim: Ibble obble,
Black bobble
Ibble obble out!
I'm It.

Helen: Hey, wait a minute – we can't play that!

Tanim: Why not?

Helen: Well, if you catch me, who's going to crawl under my legs to set me free?

Tanim: We could try and get some more people.

Helen: No, I like playing with just you.
Let's think of a different game.

(Jamie and Robin spring out.)

Jamie: Give us all your gold or we'll shoot you!

Robin: No, I say that – I'm Robin Hood, remember?

Jamie: Go on, then.

Robin: Give us all your gold or we'll shoot you!

Helen: *(Sounding bored)* Go away, you two.
We haven't got any gold.

Tanim: We're not playing Robin Hood anyway.

Jamie: What are you playing then?

Tanim: We were going to play Tunnel Tig but we haven't got enough people. Do you two want to play?

Helen: No, we're not having them. Robin's too bossy.

Robin: *(Pretending not to care)* I don't want to play stupid old Tunnel Tig anyway. Hey, look, Jamie – I mean, Little John – there are some deer over there in the forest! Let's get them!

(Robin and Jamie run off.)

Helen: I know! Let's play bank robbers!

Tanim: How do you play that?

Helen: Well, one person is the bank robber and one person is the banker, and one person is the policewoman ...

Tanim: But we've only got two people, we can't play that.

Helen: Oh dear.

Tanim: We'll have to get some more people.

(Jamie and Robin spring out again.)

Jamie: Run for your lives, you two deer! We're going to shoot you with our bows and arrows!

Robin: No, I have to say that – I'm Robin Hood, remember?

Jamie: Go on then.

Robin: Run for your lives, you two deer! We're going to shoot you with our bows and arrows!

Helen: *(Crossly)* Go away, you two. We're not deer.

Robin: Yes you are – I just heard you say, "Oh dear" to Tanim.

Helen: Oh, very funny. Anyway, we've already told you, we're not playing Robin Hood.

Jamie: Why don't you?

Tanim: *(Looking at Helen eagerly)* Yes, let's, Helen. We haven't got enough people for any of our games.

Helen: No, I'm not playing with Robin. I told you, he's too bossy.

Tanim: But I like running games.

Helen: All right, race you to the shed, then.

(Helen and Tanim race off.)

Jamie: I managed to shoot those deer, Robin.

Robin: No, you didn't, *I* did. I'm Robin Hood, remember. I'm the best one at shooting arrows. You can cook the deer for our supper if you like.

Jamie: Why don't you cook them?

Robin: I can't cook them, I'm the boss.

Jamie: Well, I've had enough of you bossing me about.

(The bell rings.)

Jamie: There's the bell. And if you think I'm playing Robin Hood again next playtime, you're wrong!

SCENE 2

The playground at lunchtime play.

(Enter Helen and Tanim.)

Tanim: What can we play with only two people?

Helen: Let's play the Yes and No game.

Tanim: How do you play that?

Helen: Well, one person asks questions and the other one has to answer them without saying Yes or No.

Tanim: All right. I'll ask the questions then. Er ... Is your name Helen?

Helen: It is.

Tanim: And ... do you like sausages?

Helen: I do.

Tanim: Are you my best friend?

Helen: Of course I am.

Tanim: You're too good at this game!
Let's think ... Do you like Jamie?

Helen: He's all right sometimes.

Tanim: Do you like Robin?

Helen: He's much too bossy. Oh no! Here he comes!

(Enter Robin and Jamie.)

Tanim: You just said No! You're out!

Jamie: Hi, Helen. Hi, Tanim.

Tanim: Are you two still playing Robin Hood?

Jamie: *(Grumpily)* No, and I'm not ever playing it again. I'm sick of always being Little John.

Robin: I know, let's play Robinson Crusoe instead. We could all play that.

Helen: No, Tanim's playing with just me.

Tanim: Hold on, Helen. Let's find out how you play it – it could be good.

Robin: Well, Robinson Crusoe gets shipwrecked and he ends up on this desert island. He has a friend called Man Friday. You can be him, Jamie.

Jamie: Why can't I be Robinson Crusoe?

Robin: Is your name Robin or something?

Jamie: What does Man Friday do?

Robin: Well, he sort of follows Robinson Crusoe around and does what he says.

Jamie: This sounds just like Robin Hood.

Robin: It's not a bit like Robin Hood, silly. We're on an *island.* Look, there are sharks all around us! You can be the sharks, Helen and Tanim.

Helen: No, we're not playing your stupid game.

Tanim: Oh, let's, Helen. It sounds better than the Yes and No game.

Helen: All right then.

Jamie: Watch out, sharks, I'm going to harpoon you!

Robin: No, I'm Robinson Crusoe, I have to say that. Watch out, sharks, I'm going to harpoon you, and Man Friday will cook you for supper!

Helen: Oh no you won't. We'll eat you for *our* supper!

Robin: No, no, you can't do that!

Tanim: Why not?

Robin: That's not in the story.

Helen: Well, we're changing the story, aren't we, Tanim?

Tanim: Yes, we're going to get you!

(They start to chase after the boys.)

Robin: No, I'm not playing if you're going to change the story. Come on, Jamie.

Jamie: *(Making up his mind)* No, why should I? I'm fed up with you, Robin. It's always, "Come on, Jamie. Do this, Jamie. Do that, Jamie." I'm staying here with the girls.

(The bell rings.)

Robin: All right, but I won't play with you next playtime.

Jamie: I don't care. I'd rather play with Helen and Tanim. You're much too bossy, Robin!

21

SCENE 3:
The playground at afternoon play.

(Enter Robin and Jamie.)

Robin: Hi, Jamie, what shall we play?

Jamie: Nothing! I'm playing with Helen and Tanim, remember?

Robin: All right, but don't expect me to play with you ever again.

(He turns away.)

Jamie: Where are you going?

Robin: Oh, I'll probably go and play football with the big boys.

(He wanders off. Enter Helen and Tanim.)

Tanim: Hi, Jamie. We're going to play "What's The Time, Mr Wolf?".

Jamie: Can I be Mr Wolf first?

Helen: Let's see.

(She "dips", starting with Jamie.)

Helen: Dip, dip, sky blue, who's It? Not you!
You're out, Jamie.
Dip, dip, sky blue, who's It? Not you!
You're Mr Wolf, Tanim. Come on, Jamie.

(They walk along behind Tanim.)

Jamie and Helen: What's the time, Mr Wolf?

Tanim: Four o'clock.

Jamie and Helen: What's the time, Mr Wolf?

Tanim: Half-past eleven.

Jamie and Helen: What's the time, Mr Wolf?

Tanim: Dinner time!

(She chases them and catches Helen.)

Tanim: Got you, Helen! Your turn to be Mr Wolf. Come on, Jamie.

Jamie and Tanim:	What's the time, Mr Wolf?
Helen:	Eight o'clock.
Jamie and Tanim:	What's the time, Mr Wolf?
Helen:	Quarter-past five.
Jamie and Tanim:	What's the time, Mr Wolf?
Helen:	Dinner time!
	(She chases them and catches Tanim.)
Helen:	Got you, Tanim!

(Enter Robin, looking rather miserable.)

Robin: Can I play?

Helen: No! You're too bossy.

Robin: Oh, go on.

Jamie: I thought you were going to play football with the big boys.

Robin: *(Rather embarrassed)* They wouldn't let me. They said I was too young, and they said I was ... oh, never mind.

Tanim: What did they say you were?

Robin: They said I was a rotten runner.

Helen: *(Delighted)* Well, you are! Robin is a slowcoach, Robin is a slowcoach!

Jamie: Don't be mean. He's not a slowcoach.

Helen: Well, he can't play anyway, can he, Tanim?

Tanim: Why don't we give him another chance?

Helen: No, we don't want a fat old slowcoach playing with us. Round Robin, round Robin!

Jamie: *(Getting cross)* Don't be so nasty. He's my friend.

Tanim: Oh, go on, let him.

Helen: No, he can't. Silly Robin Redbreast! Silly Robin Redbreast!

Jamie: *(Really angry now)* I think you're being really horrible. I'm not going to play with you any more.

Helen: Don't, then!

Tanim: *(Pleading)* Oh yes, do!

Helen: It's nearly the end of playtime anyway. Come on, Tanim, let's see if we can be the first in the line.

(Helen and Tanim go off.)

Robin: Thanks, Jamie. You were really nice.

Jamie: Well, I was getting fed up with "What's The Time, Mr Wolf?" anyway. It's a bit of a baby game, and I never even got to be Mr Wolf.

Robin: Will you play with me now, then?

Jamie: It all depends.

Robin: Depends on what?

Jamie: On whether you're going to boss me about all the time.

Robin: I won't, I promise. I know, you can choose which game to play.

Jamie: All right then.

(There is a pause while Jamie thinks.)

Robin: Have you decided yet?

Jamie: I'm just thinking.

Robin: Remember, if there's anyone called Robin in it I have to be him, because my name really is Robin.

Jamie: *(Looking pleased)* That's just given me a brilliant idea.

(The bell rings.)

Jamie: Oh, there's the bell.

Robin: Never mind, we can play it tomorrow. What is it?

Jamie: Batman and Robin!

(He runs off, followed by Robin.)